OFFICIAL ANNUA

Colour in Duke's head for every time you find his name in the grid. Look horizontally and vertically.

D	E	D	D	E	U	K	D
E	D	U	E	K	D	E	U
K	D	K	U	D	U	K	E
U	K	E	D	K	E	D	K
D	D	U	E	K	U	U	D
U	K	D	D	U	K	E	U
K	U	U	E	K	D	U	K
E	D	K	D	U	K	E	K

Draw your self-portrait.

Captain Bennett asked Harl to design a police drone.
Do you know how to finish the picture?

In his free time Harl enjoys playing dominoes.
Where should the numbered tiles be placed?

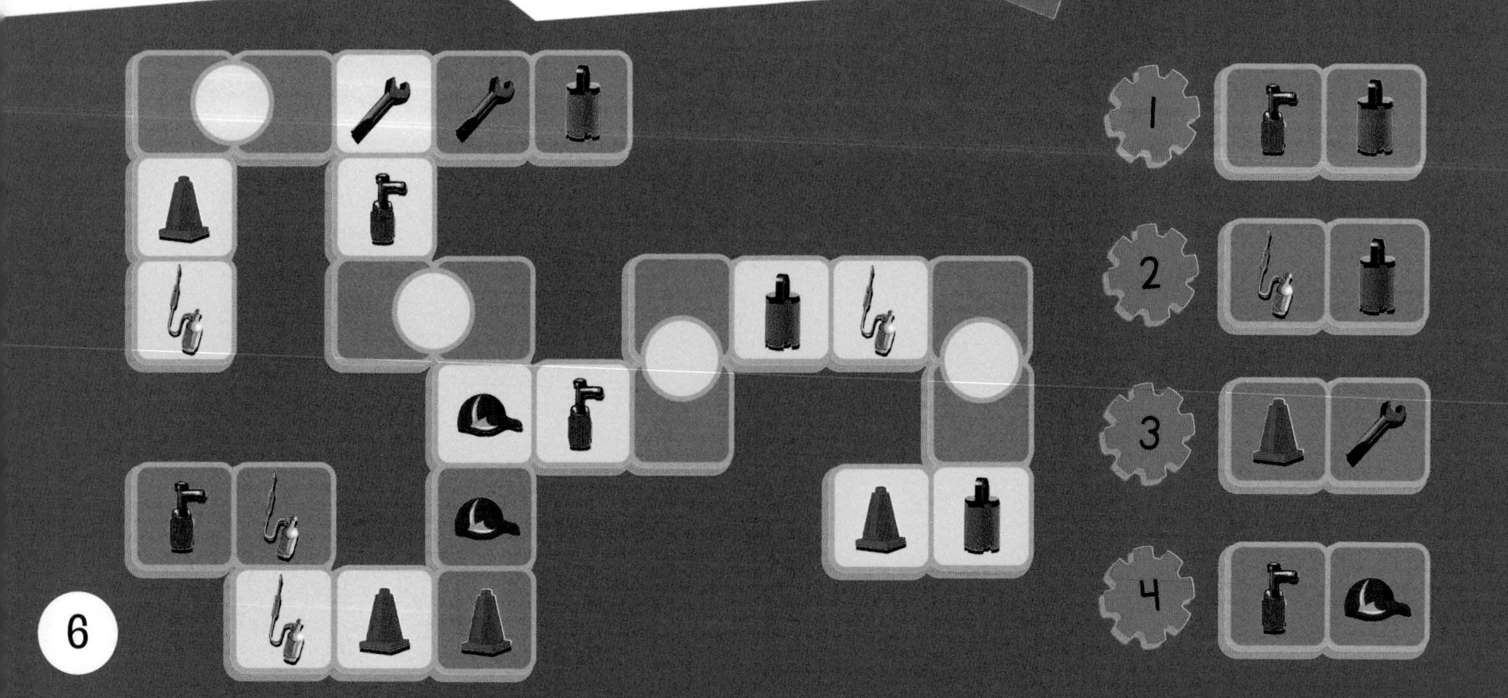

Mark the equipment the Sky Police might need.

BLAST OFF TO JAIL!

Everything is going to plan. Hacksaw Hank and Big Betty steal a safe from the bank and all is going smoothly until … their car breaks down!

"What now?" Betty shouts.

Suddenly a vehicle loaded with junk and spare parts appears in the street. Its smiling owner stops when he sees the crooks.

"Do you need a hand?" he calls out to them. "Helpful Harl here. Happy to help!"

"Our car broke down and we're … umm," Betty stutters.
"Safe maintenance!" adds Hank quickly. "We … umm … need to maintain it!"

"He means repair it," says Betty.

"No problem!" laughs Harl. "You must be in a hurry then!" Soon the street fills with sounds of hammering, sawing, bolting, cracking and rattling.

Finally, Harl reveals the car with two enormous rocket engines attached to the roof. The crooks jump with joy.

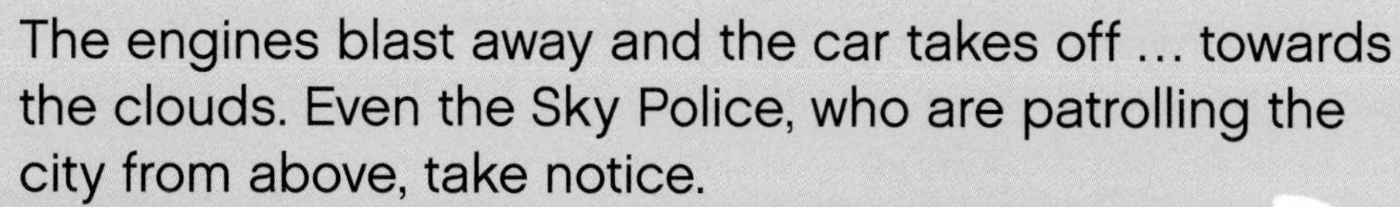

The engines blast away and the car takes off … towards the clouds. Even the Sky Police, who are patrolling the city from above, take notice.

"Hey!" says police officer Rooky. "Is that a flying car?"
"Cars don't fly!" growls Sam Grizzled, who is looking the other way.

Meanwhile, the crooks' car takes a dive.
"Stop this thing!" Betty screams.
Hank slams the brakes, the car stops and …

It lands with a loud thud next to the police station!

"I can't believe it!" says Duke DeTain. "Our stolen safe together with the robbers!" Then he looks around and adds, "OK, let's grab them ... the kids are watching."

As the police officers lead the crooks away to jail, Harl Hubbs passes by.

"It's him!" cries Betty. "It's all because of him!"

"Thanks!" Duke calls out to Harl.

"Happy to help!" answers the handyman happily.

Draw what else Duke DeTain is thinking about.

The gang has stolen three vehicles to carry out the crime of the century! Untangle the lines to help Duke match the crook to the car.

Which object appears most often in the grid?
It's something every crook always keeps handy.

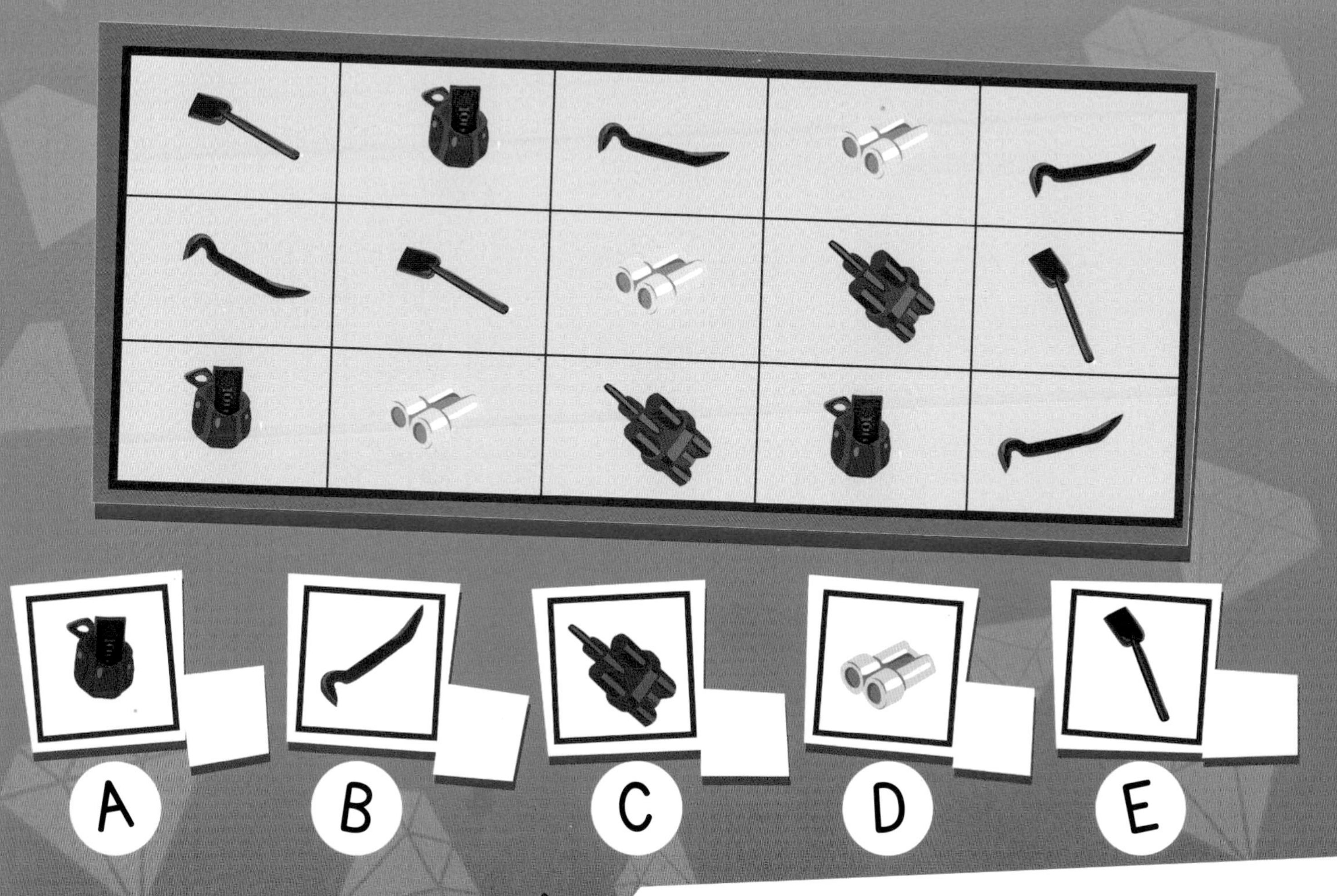

Draw the faces Hacksaw Hank makes in different situations.

When planning another hold-up.

After stealing a safe with precious jewels.

After being caught by Duke DeTain.

Finish drawing Duke's car using the example.

Can you catch the crook speeding through town in a big car? They appear in the grid three times.

In each row, mark the character that is different from the others.

Which of Chief Wheeler's shadows is the right one?

How many police dogs are helping solve crimes? Write the number below.

LUNCH BREAK

Finally! Time for my lunch break!

Cross out the letters in the grid that appear more than once to reveal the crook Duke has arrested.
D C F O U B
Y R S T Z Q
O W A D C M
J N Z D B S
Y Q K P T J
B I U M W Z
P C E J B U
How could I get myself caught?
Quick police thinking! Match the pieces to the empty spaces.
A
B
C
D
E
LCH
HK60243

Draw as many banknotes on the page as you can!

How to draw Feldman?

Practise here!

Use a mirror to read the names of the brave women who work alongside Duke to maintain order in LEGO® City.
FREYA
ROOKY
SHIRLEY
Lead Duke to the crook's car by untangling the paths.
A
B
C

Complete the sketches of the crook.

Draw Duke's portrait following the instructions.

The LEGO City Police Chief should be:

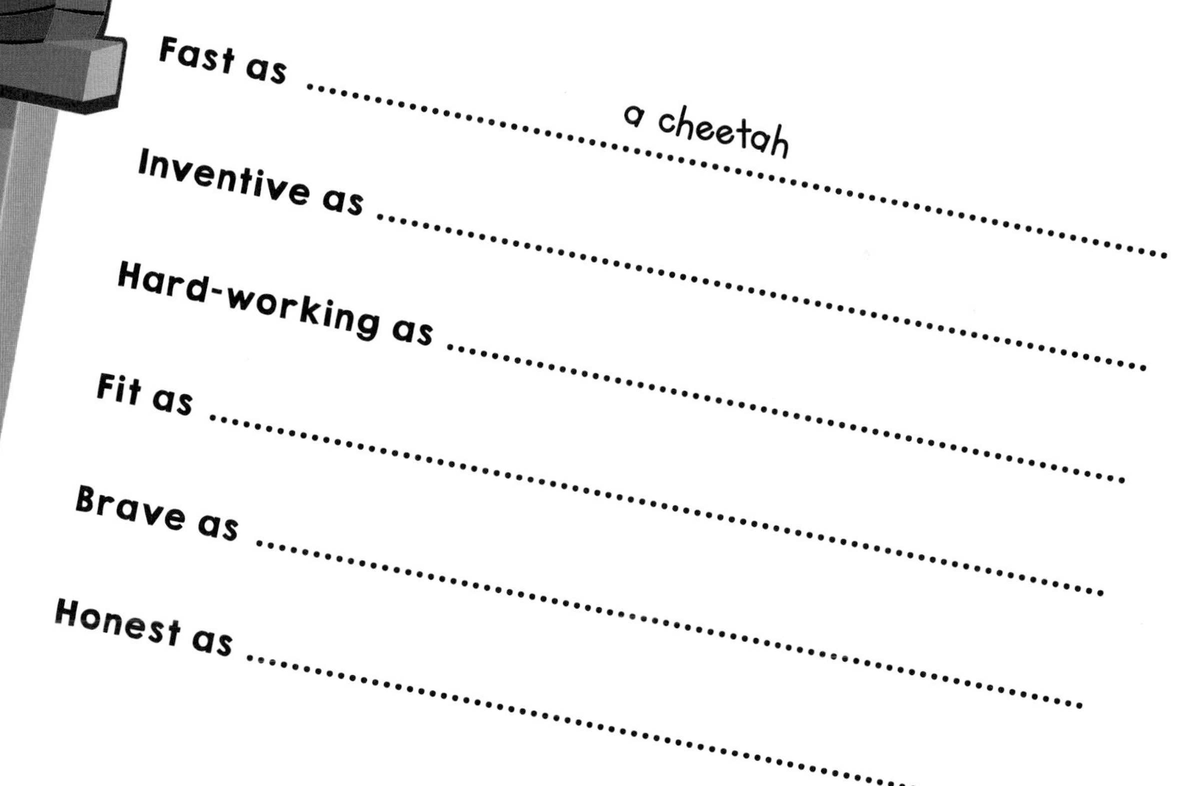

Fast as .... a cheetah ....

Inventive as ....

Hard-working as ....

Fit as ....

Brave as ....

Honest as ....

....

Finish the comic by adding your words to the speech bubbles.

BANK

SAFE INC.

Look at the picture pieces on the right and mark the ones that don't match the team picture of the sky and ground police on the left.

Connect the dots to see what officer Rooky's favourite jet looks like.

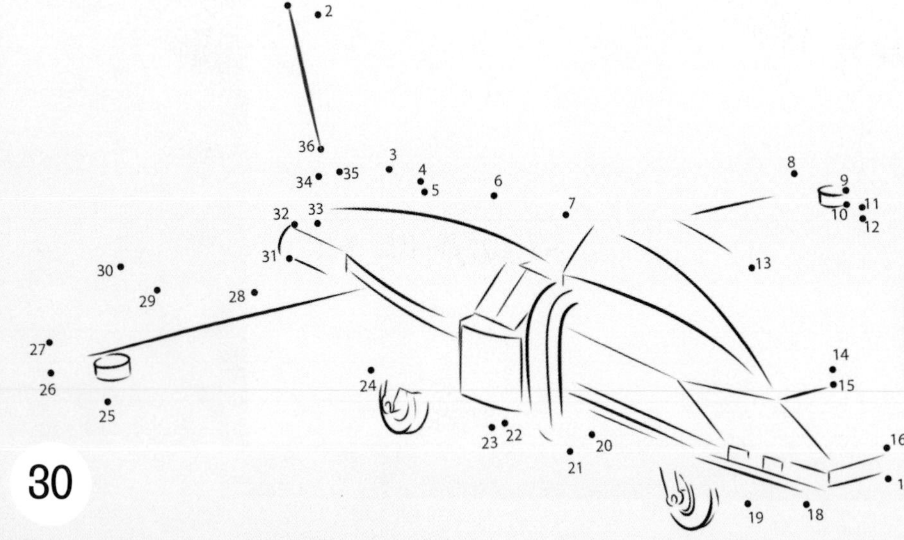

Follow the sequence shown to help the Sky Police catch the crooks on the passenger plane.

Colour in the Sky Police jet.

Connect the parts with the right vehicles stolen by a gang of thieves.

Captain Bennett chose the team to work at the Inventions Through History Parade. Look closely at the characters on the screen for 15 seconds and turn the page.

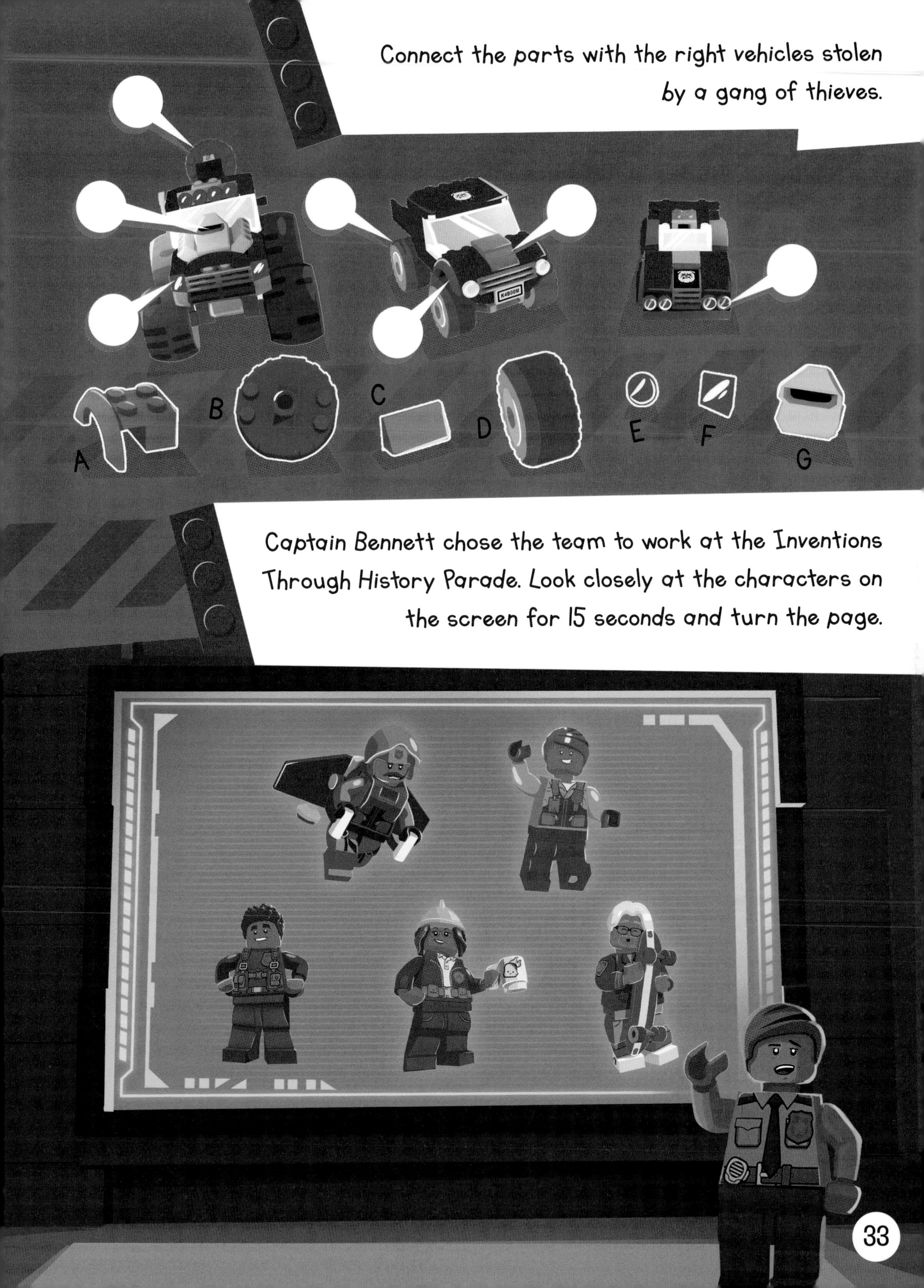

Circle the characters enjoying the parade. Hint: They didn't appear on the previous page.

Match each of Duke DeTain's crooks with the object they stole.

Practise here!

#1
MAYOR

Draw what else Mayor Fleck is thinking about.

Who is the dangerous crook unmasked by Harl?
Untangle the lines to find out!

Complete the grid so the vehicles don't appear more than once in any row, column or outlined area.

1	2	3	4	5

Look at the two pictures of the police in action and find eight differences between them.

Mark five crooks on the picture so the police officers know where to find them.

Harl serviced Sky Police officer Rooky's jet. Do you know which shadow belongs to the vehicle?

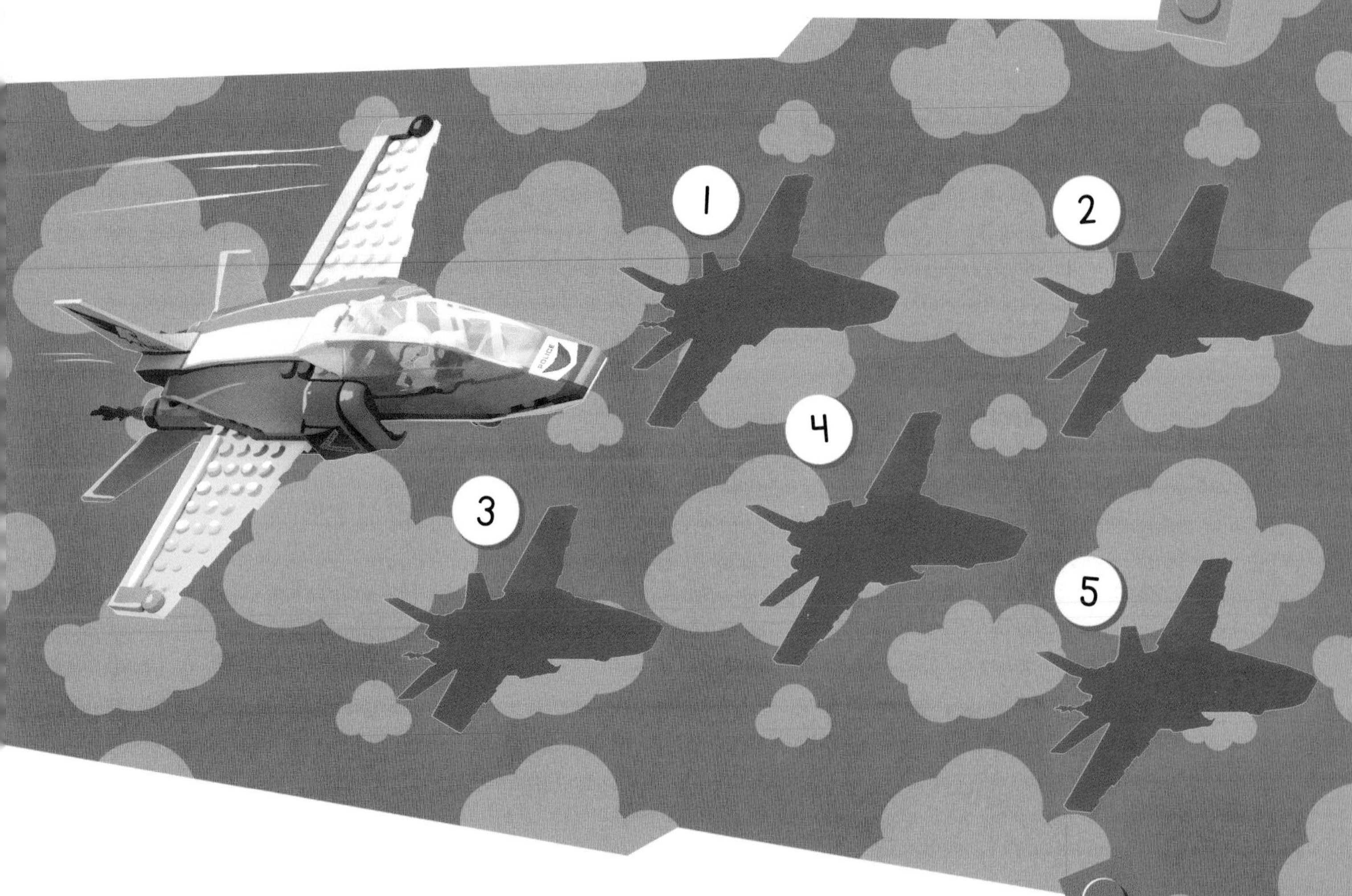

Who is missing out on Harl's help in each row? Write the correct numbers in the empty spaces.

Design new outfits for the LEGO City Mayor!

THE ONLY WAY IS UP

After a chase with the LEGO City police, two crooks named Daisy and Frankie smash into a fire hydrant. Water sprays everywhere.

"Ha! I said you can't escape!" says Officer Duke DeTain.

Duke puts the crooks into his patrol car for a trip to the police station.
"Enjoy the ride," says Duke, "before the police helicopter takes you to prison."

Duke speeds off.

"Too fast!" shout Daisy and Frankie, closing their eyes.

Suddenly, the helicopter pilot calls. "That fire hydrant flooded the ground!" he says. "I can't land!"

The crooks smile. If the helicopter can't land, it can't take them to prison!

"Meet me on top of LEGO City's tallest building!" Duke says.
"Erm … Roger that!" the pilot replies.

Duke drives towards the tallest building.
"You're going to crash!" shouts Frankie.

But they don't crash! Instead, they drive right up the side!
D3TA1N
The patrol car jumps one building, then another! "Let us out!" shouts Daisy.
POLICE
WHOOSH!

The patrol car lands on the roof of the tallest building in LEGO City. "I'm done," says Daisy. "Take me to prison!"
WHUMP!
"No helicopters!" says Frankie. "No more flying!"
POLICE
D3TA1N
"Okay," Duke says. "I'll drive you to prison instead!"
The crooks run for the helicopter, shouting, "Anything but that!"

Help Harl illuminate Poppy's stage. Colour lights that haven't been lit yet with the correct colour.

How many hammers do you see? Write the answer below.

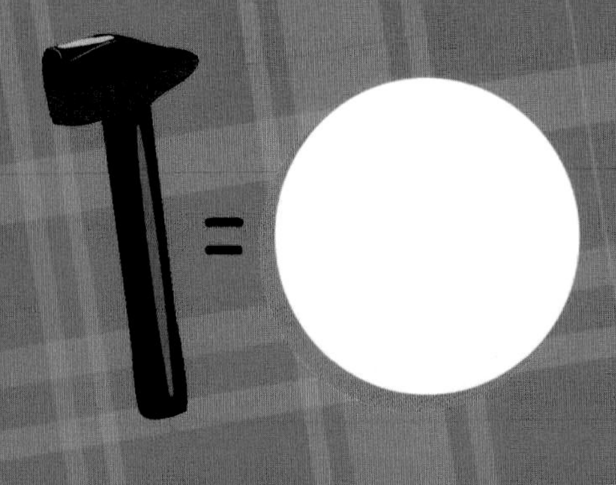

Match the close-ups to the vehicles. Write the numbers in the empty spaces.

Plan an adventure!

How will you get there?
54
Draw the treasure you'll find there!

Design your own funky mug!

What will you drink in it?

....

....

Look at Roastie and show Harl the right set of spare parts for the intelligent firefighting robot.

Find two identical Harl faces.

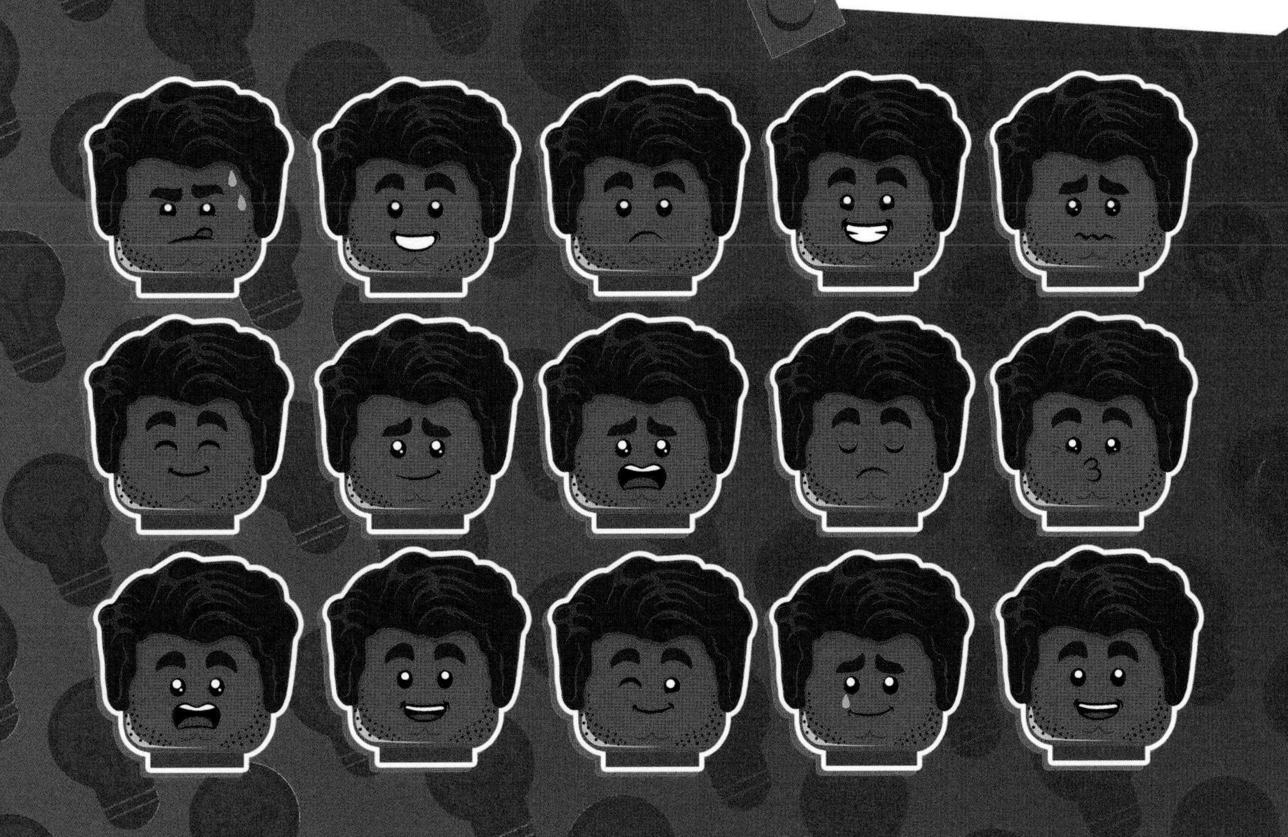

THE HEIST

Three crooks have just broken into the LEGO City bank ...

I got it open!
It is I! Duke DeTain, in the flesh!

But why were you hiding inside that safe?

Because I love a surprise!

Design a cool door for your room!

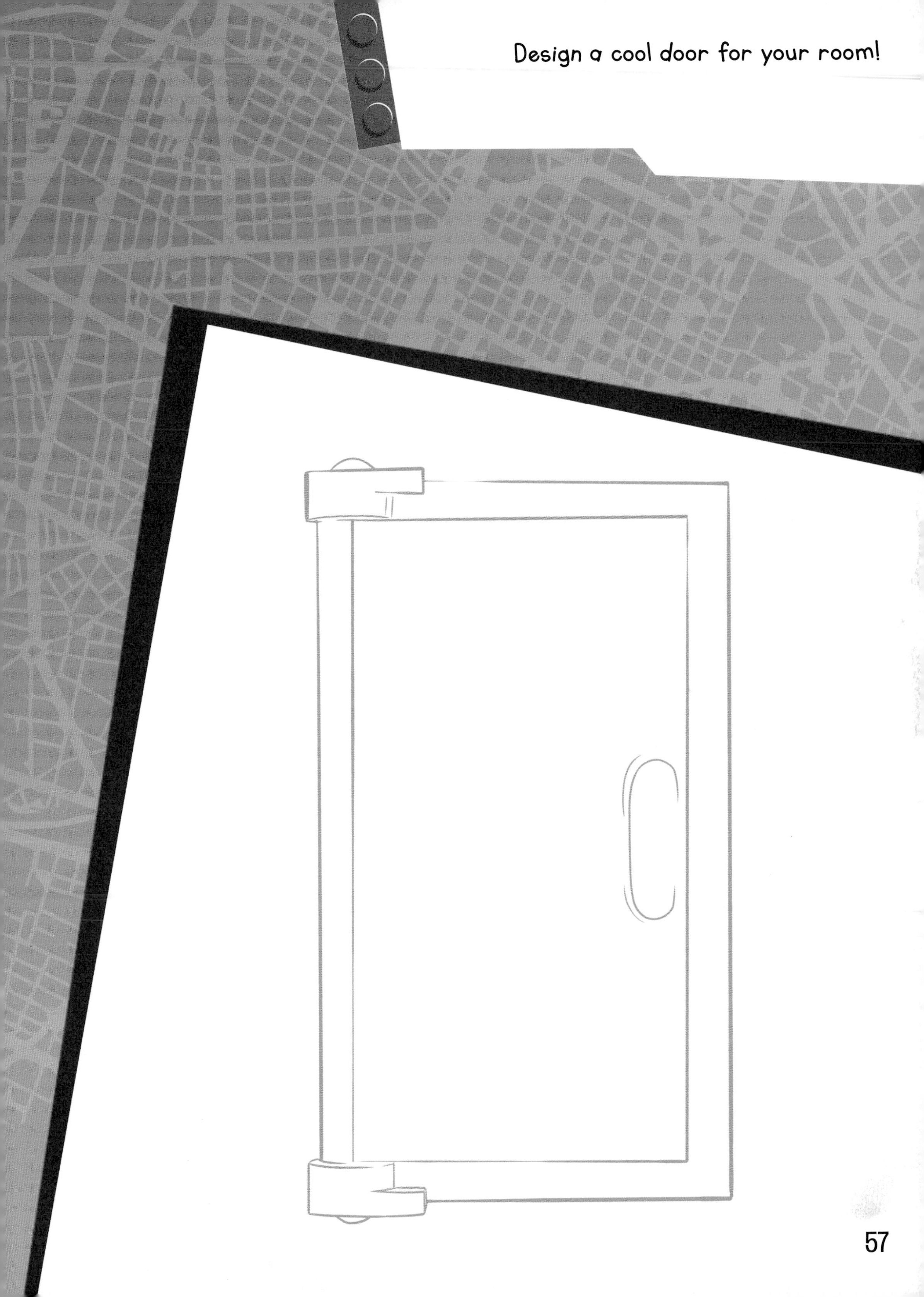

ANSWERS

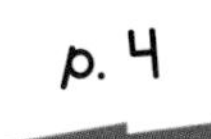
p. 4

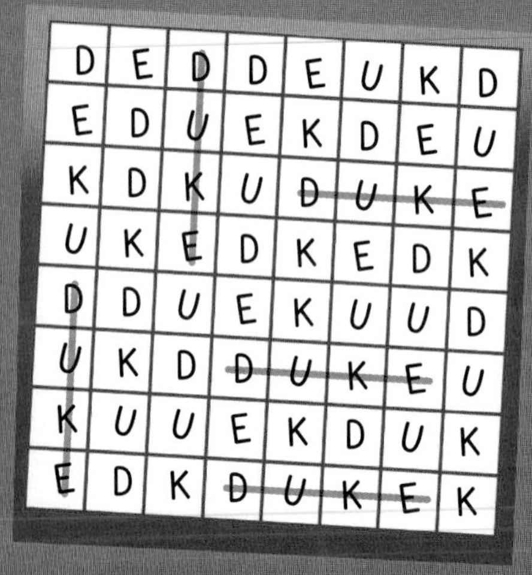

p. 6

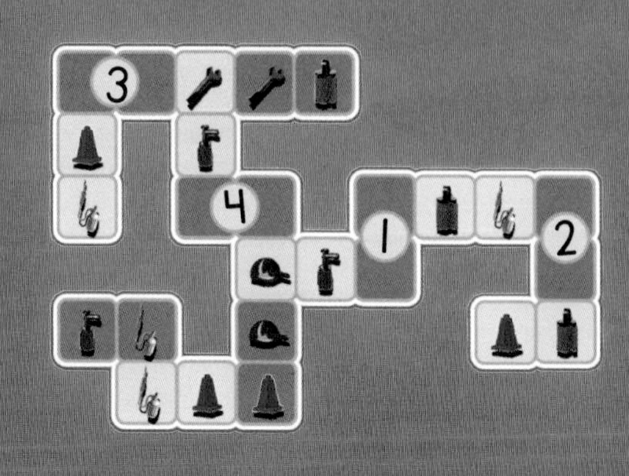

p. 7

p. 14

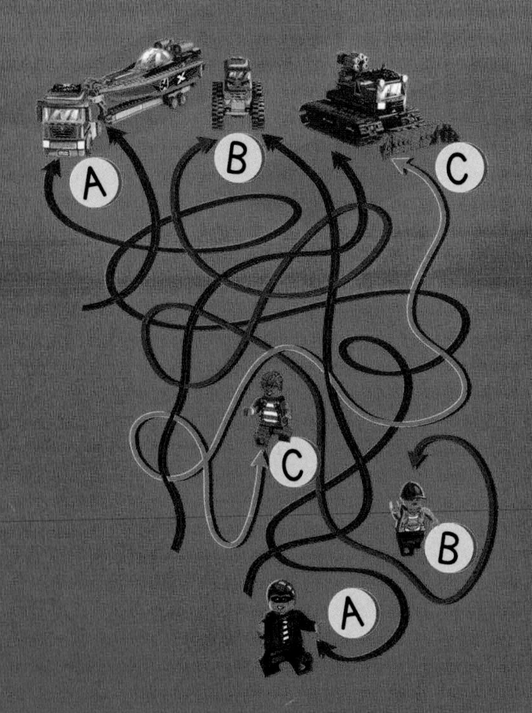

p. 15

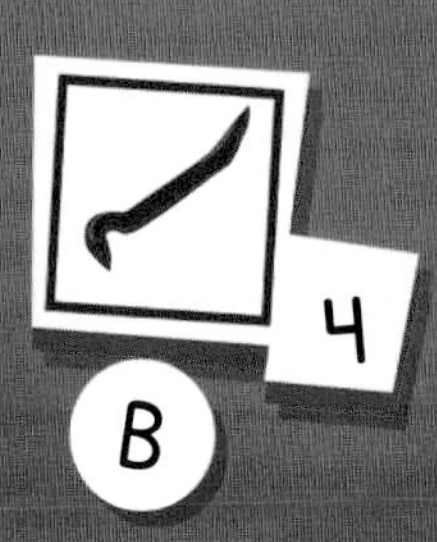

p. 17

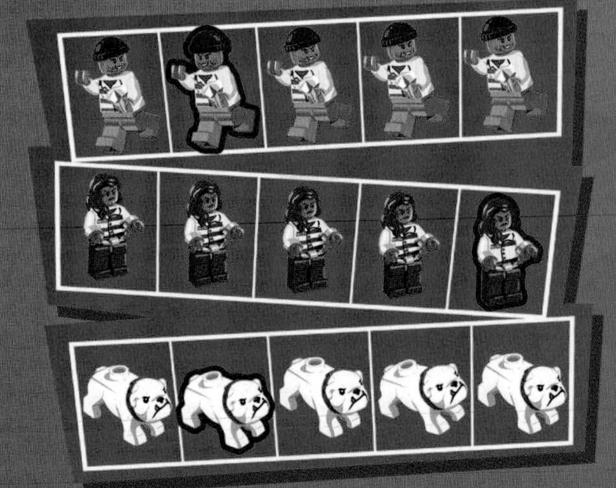

p. 18

4

6

p. 20

FRANKIE

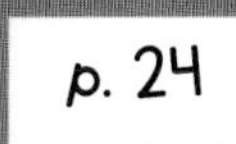

p. 24

FREYA

ROOKY

SHIRLEY

B

p. 30

p. 30

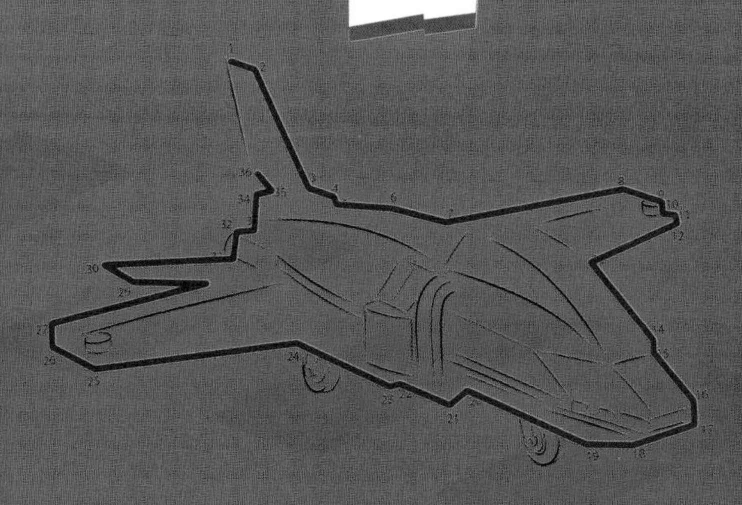

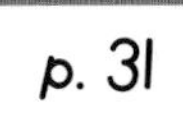

p. 31

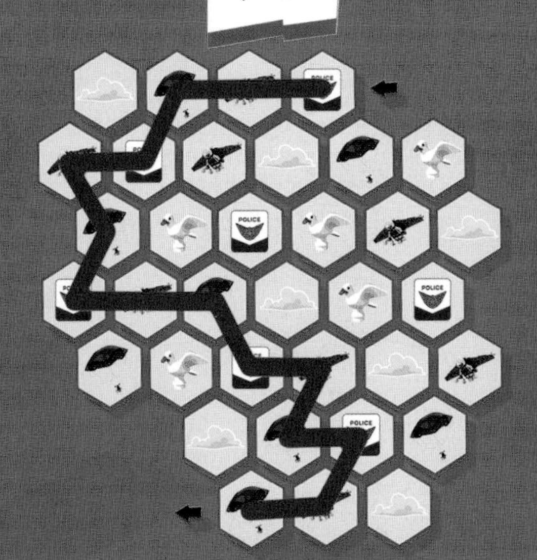

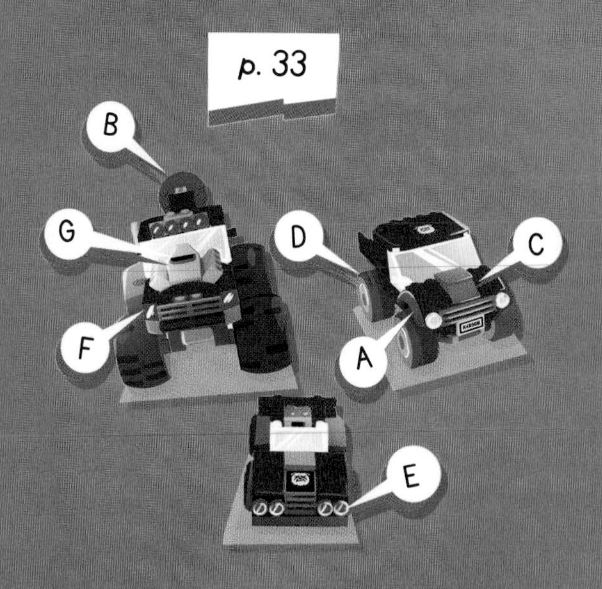

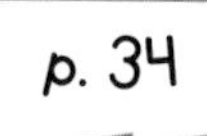

p. 38

p. 39

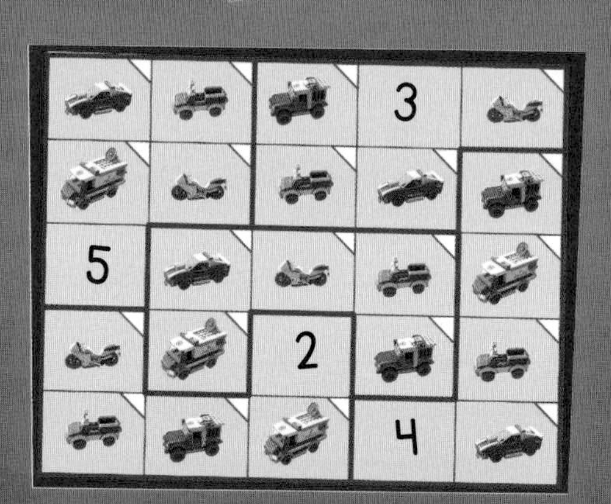

pp. 40-41

p. 42

p. 48

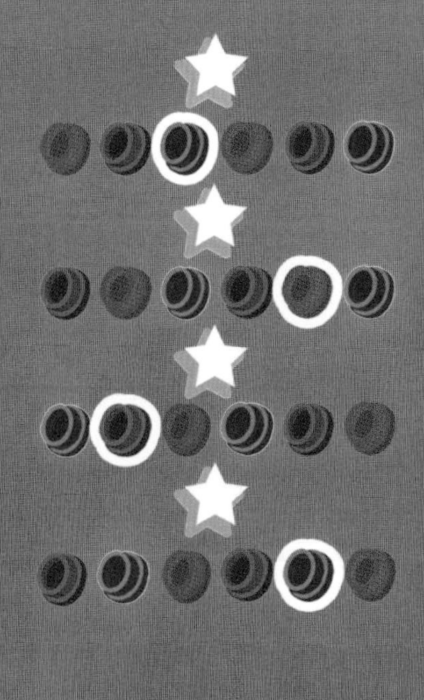

p. 49

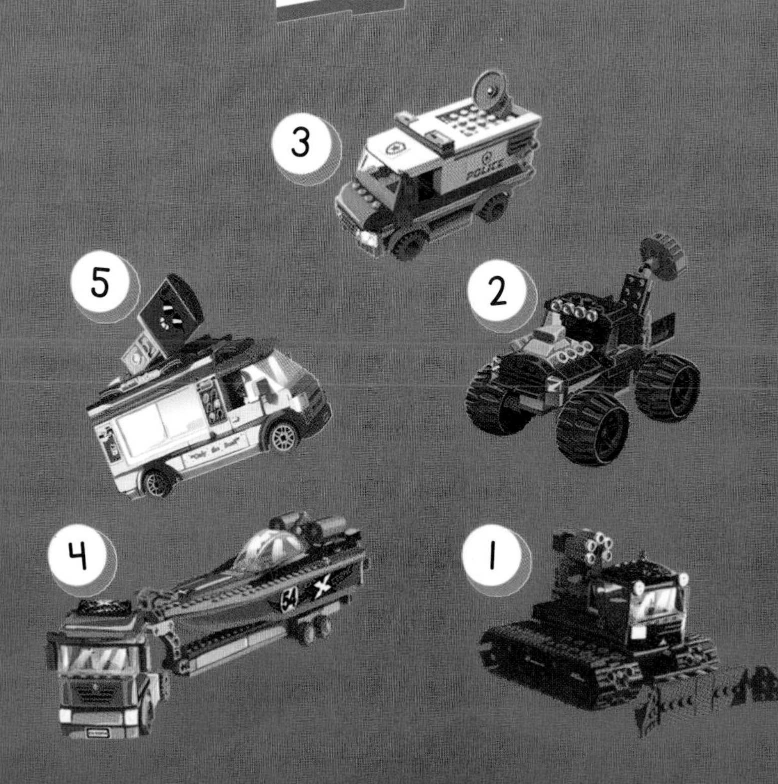

p. 53

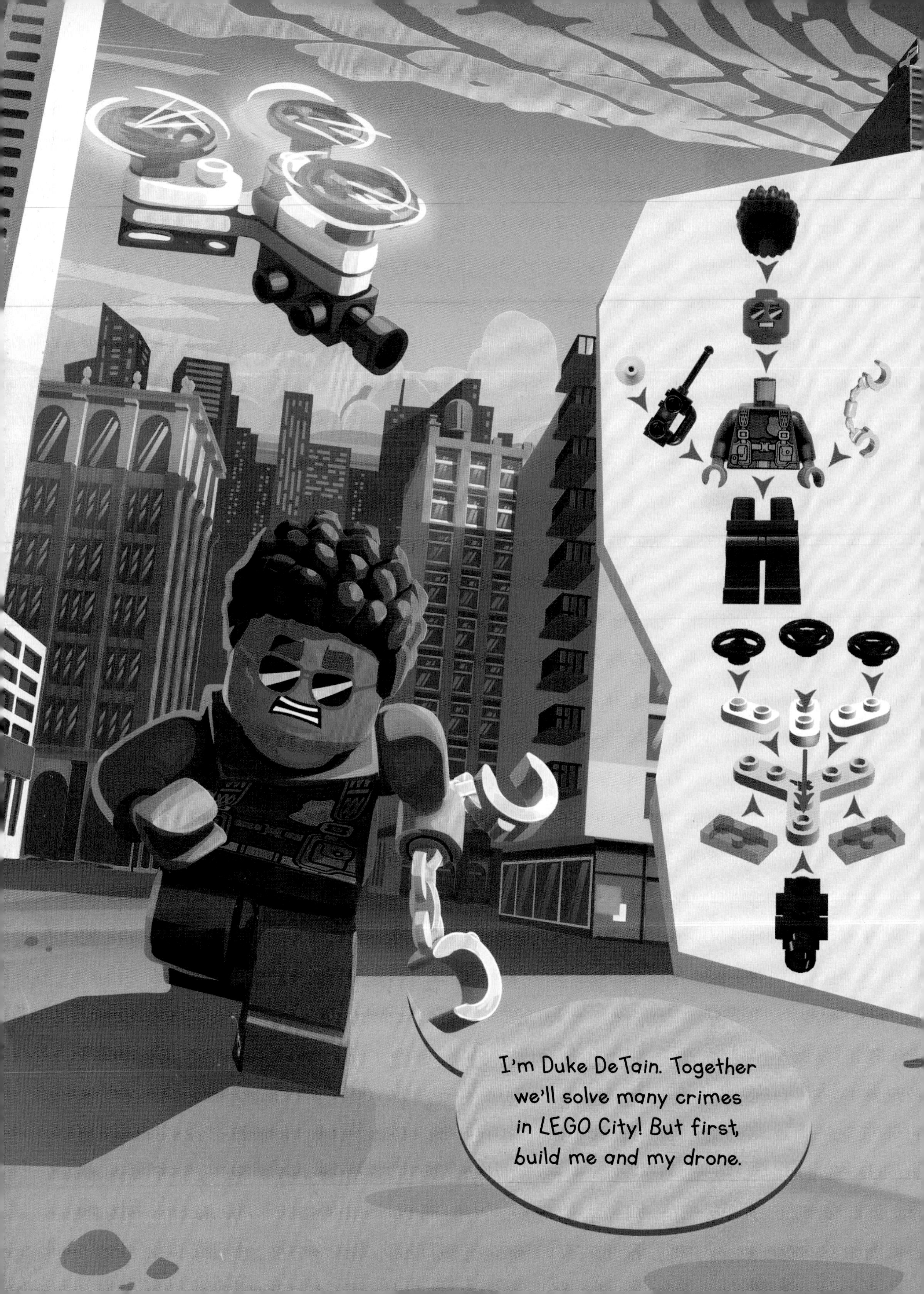
I'm Duke DeTain. Together we'll solve many crimes in LEGO City! But first, build me and my drone.